CONTENTS

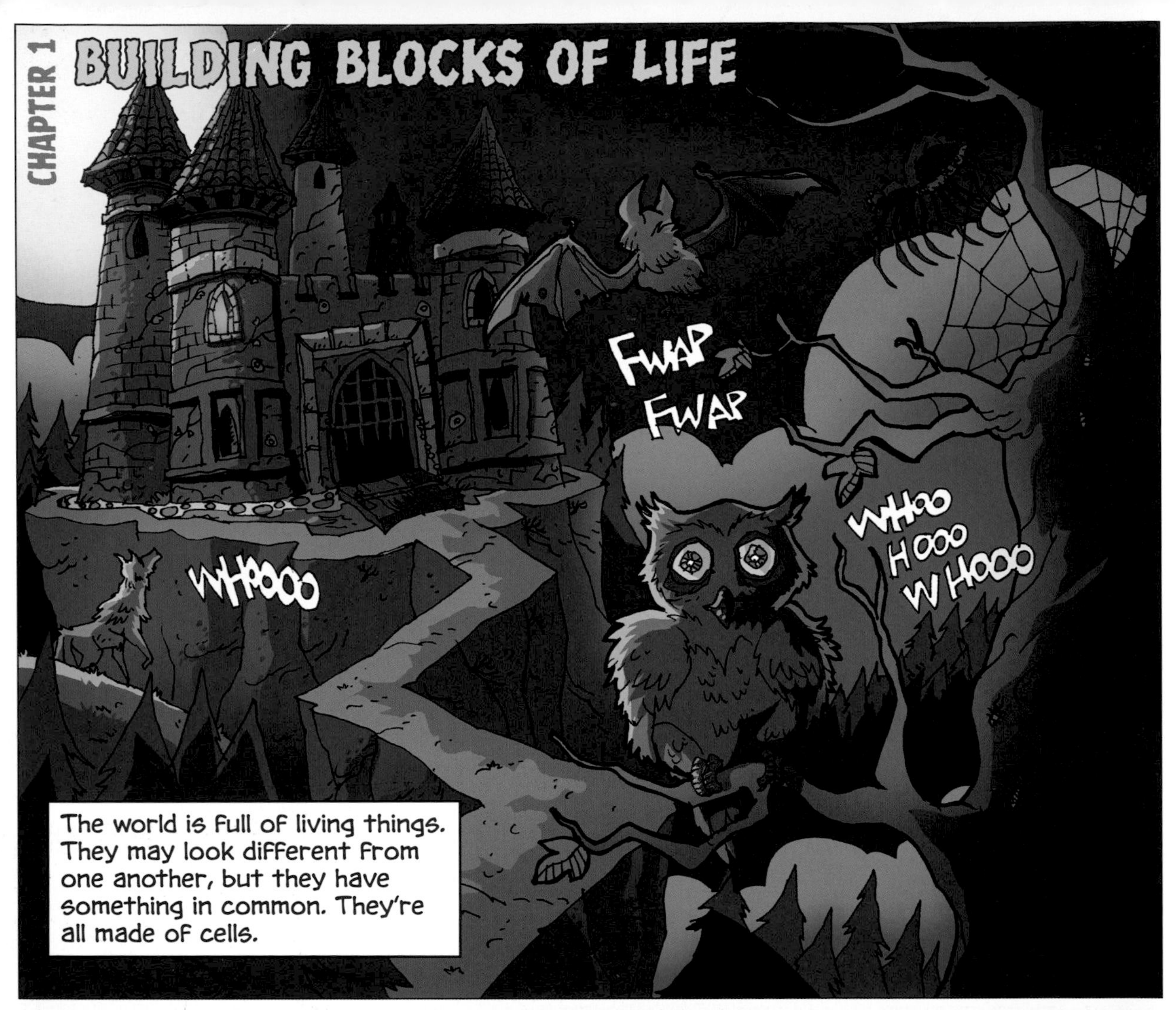
CHAPTER 1
BUILDING BLOCKS OF LIFE
FWAP
FWAP
WHOOO
WHOO
HOOO
WHOOO
The world is full of living things. They may look different from one another, but they have something in common. They're all made of cells.

SLAM
?!
Ivy, wolves, and bats are all made up of cells. Cells are the basic building blocks of life.

Every living thing is made up of one or more cells. Bacteria are each made up of a single cell.
Other living things, such as plants and animals, are made up of many cells working together. Your body has more than 10 trillion cells!
AND ALL 10 TRILLION HURT!

Most cells are tiny. They are too small to be seen with the human eye. That's why scientists didn't know cells existed until about 350 years ago.
THEY'RE EVEN TOO SMALL FOR VAMPIRE EYES!

The first person to see cells was British scientist Robert Hooke.
In 1665, Hooke used a microscope to look at a thin slice of cork from the bark of an oak tree.
HiSSSS

Hooke saw tiny, hollow structures that looked like little rooms. He called these structures "cells" because they reminded him of the rooms that monks lived in.
WHERE ARE THE RED BLOOD CELLS?

A few years later, Dutch lens maker Antony van Leeuwenhoek started looking at things under a microscope, too. His microscope magnified objects more than 200 times.
WHO USED MY MICROSCOPE?

Leeuwenhoek was the first person to see and describe living cells, including bacteria. He called them "animalcules," which means tiny animals.
DO THEY HAVE TINY NECKS?
WOW, TINY ANIMALS!

Since then, scientists have discovered a lot more about cells.
EVEN RED BLOOD CELLS?

Cells come in many types, shapes, and sizes. Most cells are tiny – about 0.0025 centimetre (0.001 inch) wide.
I WANT TO SUCK YOUR BLUH .... ERR .... BORROW YOUR MICROSCOPE.

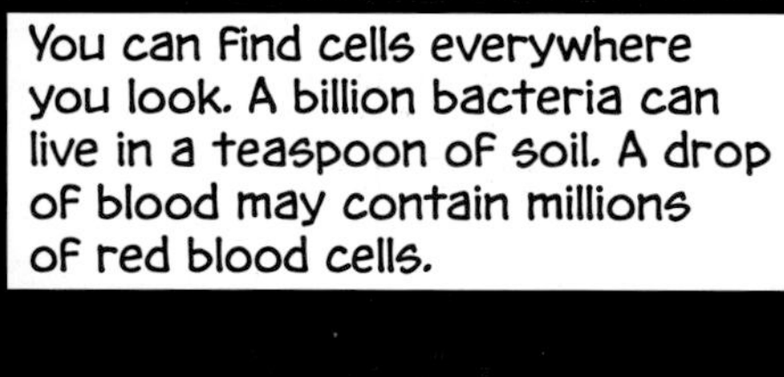
You can find cells everywhere you look. A billion bacteria can live in a teaspoon of soil. A drop of blood may contain millions of red blood cells.

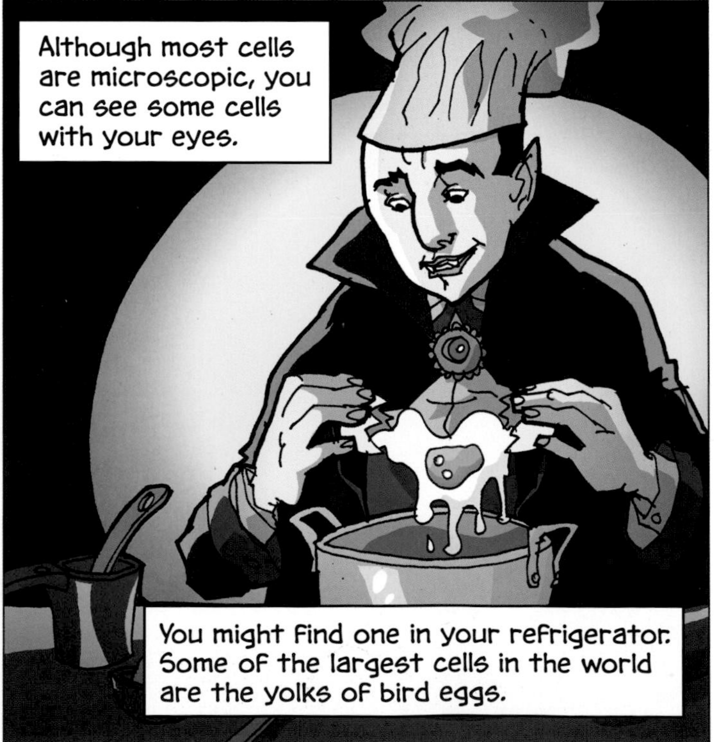
Although most cells are microscopic, you can see some cells with your eyes.
You might find one in your refrigerator. Some of the largest cells in the world are the yolks of bird eggs.

One monster-sized cell belongs to the ostrich. Before it begins to develop, an ostrich egg consists of a single cell that can be more than 15 centimetres (6 inches) in length!
TUC
TUC
TUC
?

Cells come in a variety of shapes, including coils, boxes, corkscrews, rods, or balls.
IS THAT A WOODEN STAKE?

The microscopic, single-celled amoeba has no specific shape at all. It's a jelly-like mass that moves by changing its shape.
TRY CHANGING INTO A BAT!

CHAPTER 2

CELLS WORKING TOGETHER

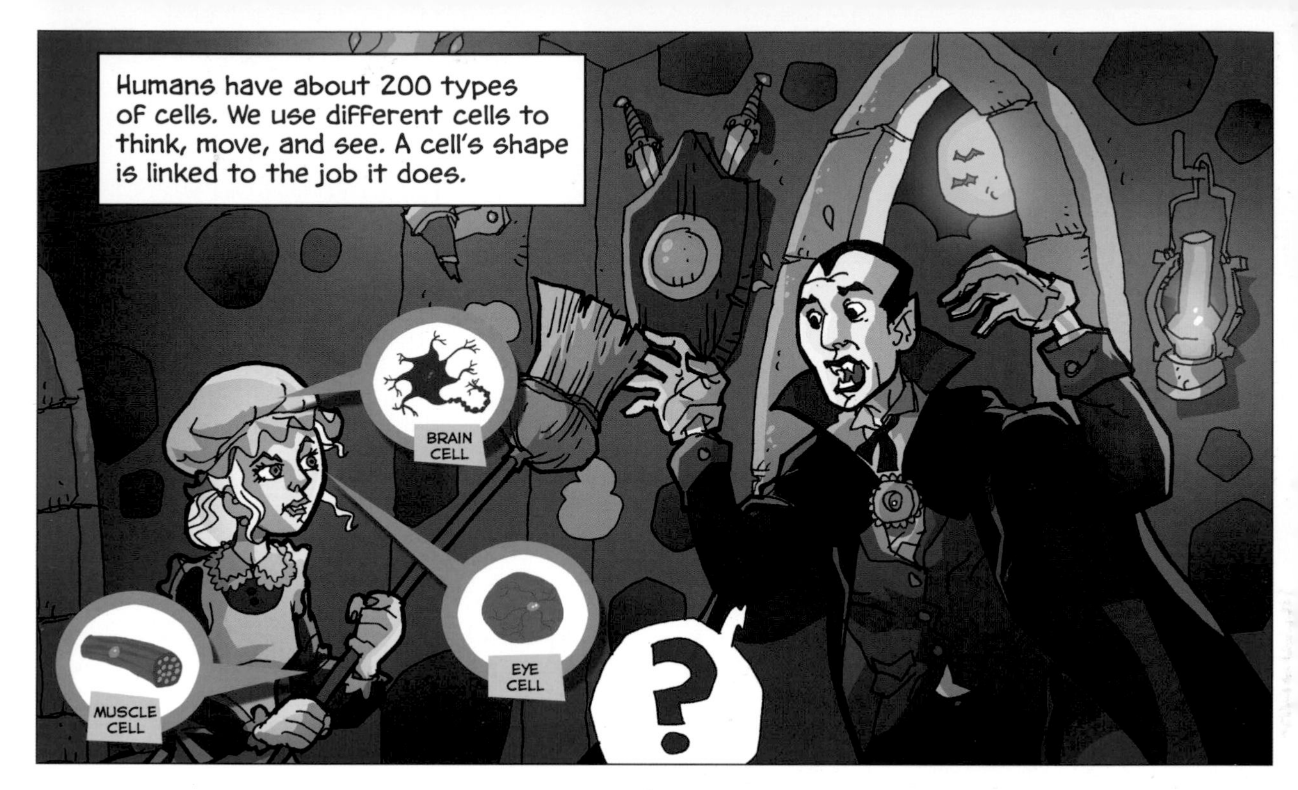
Humans have about 200 types of cells. We use different cells to think, move, and see. A cell's shape is linked to the job it does.
BRAIN CELL
EYE CELL
MUSCLE CELL
?

Fat cells look like bubbles. They help keep your body warm and store energy.
BOING
BOING
BOING
TIP
TIP
TIP
Muscle cells are long and stringy so they can contract to do work.
Nerve cells have many branches that can receive messages from other nerve cells.

All types of cells work together to form a living thing. Groups of cells that work together to do a specific job are called tissues.
Muscle cells, for example, join together to form muscle tissue.

Organs are two or more tissues that work together. Some examples of organs are brains, hearts, and livers.
THIS ISN'T THE TYPE OF ORGAN YOU MEANT?

WHAT ABOUT PLANTS?

Plants have different types of cells that also form tissues. One tissue forms the hard outer covering of trees called bark. Plant tissues also make up plant organs, such as leaves, stems, and roots.

CHAPTER 3
CELLS UP CLOSE
All cells are divided into two main groups – eukaryotic and prokaryotic. Eukaryotic cells have a structure called the nucleus where the DNA is stored. These cells also have membrane-covered structures called organelles that do specific jobs in the cell.
TASTES EUKARYOTIC TO ME.
FWAP
FWAP

Prokaryotic cells don't have a nucleus. Their DNA floats freely within the cell. They also lack membrane-covered organelles.
DEFINITELY A PROKARYOTIC FLAVOUR.
?
FWAP
FWAP

DNA genetic material that carries all of the instructions to make a living thing and keep it working; DNA stands for deoxyribonucleic acid

organelle structure in the cell that carries out cell activities

Cells come in many shapes and sizes and do different things. But they also have a few things in common. Cells take in food, get rid of waste, grow, and reproduce. And cells, like all living things, eventually die.

Each cell is surrounded by a cell membrane. The membrane acts as a barrier between the inside of the cell and the environment it is in. The cell membrane controls what comes in and out of the cell.

Cells also have organelles. Just like the organs in your body perform certain jobs, organelles perform specific tasks within the cell.
?
HMMM ... HOW CAN I GET IN THERE?

POOF
FWAP FWAP

IT DIDN'T SAY BATS WEREN'T ALLOWED!
BLOTCH

In all cells, the chemicals and structures are surrounded by fluid. The fluid and almost everything in it is called cytoplasm.

Animal cells have a variety of organelles. Each organelle has a job to do.
NUCLEUS: The control centre of the cell that houses the cell's chromosomes.
NUCLEOLUS: A region found inside the nucleus that helps make ribosomes.
RIBOSOMES: Tiny bodies in the cell that help make proteins. Proteins allow the cell to grow and repair itself.
LYSOSOMES: Structures that digest food particles, waste, and foreign objects.
FWAP
FWAP
CHROMOSOMES: Structures that contain the information to operate and copy the cell. Chromosomes are made of DNA.
ENDOPLASMIC RETICULUM: A network of membranes that transports materials in the cell.
GOLGI COMPLEX: An organelle that holds and moves proteins and other materials to other parts of the cell or outside the cell membrane.

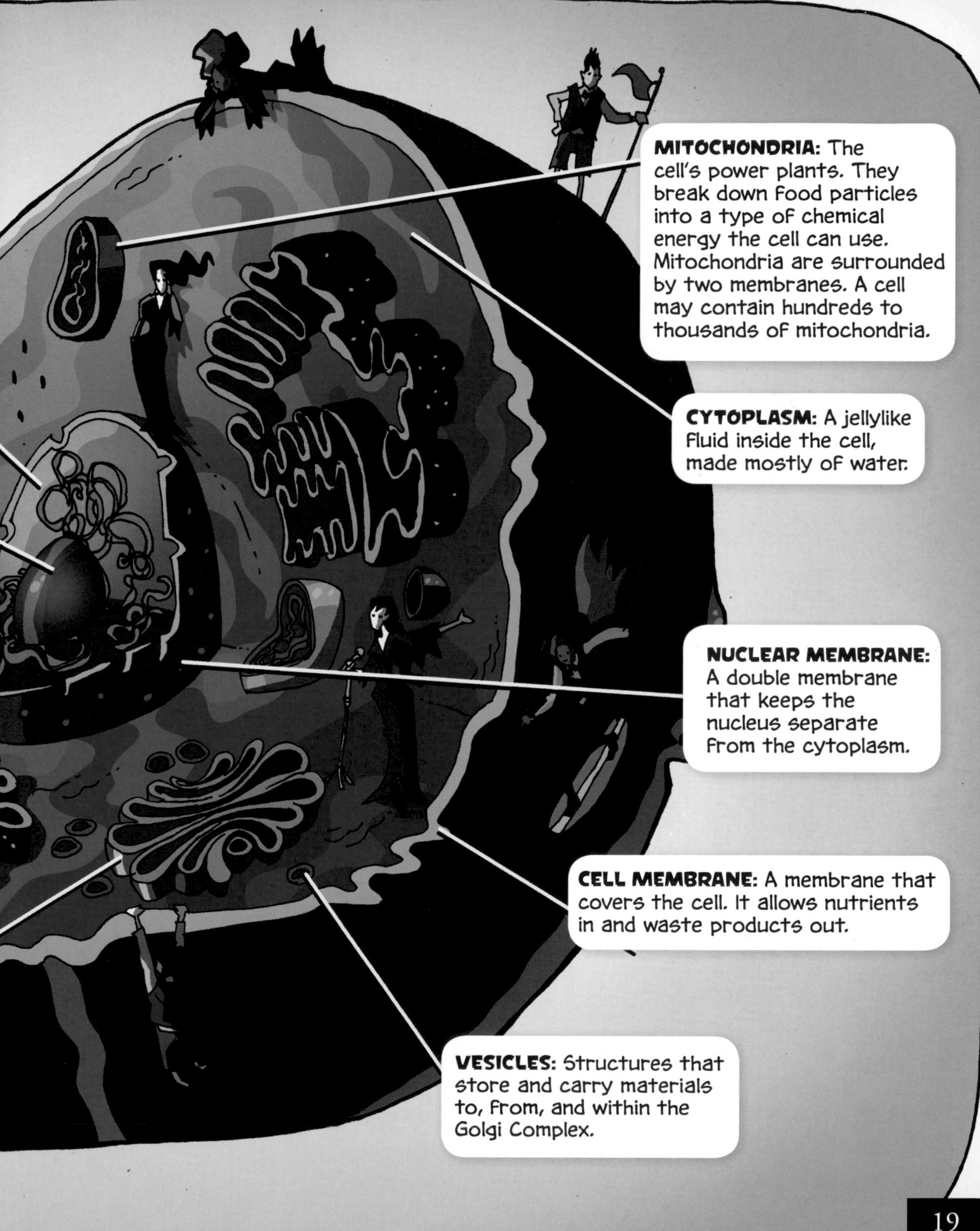
MITOCHONDRIA: The cell's power plants. They break down food particles into a type of chemical energy the cell can use. Mitochondria are surrounded by two membranes. A cell may contain hundreds to thousands of mitochondria.
CYTOPLASM: A jellylike fluid inside the cell, made mostly of water.
NUCLEAR MEMBRANE: A double membrane that keeps the nucleus separate from the cytoplasm.
CELL MEMBRANE: A membrane that covers the cell. It allows nutrients in and waste products out.
VESICLES: Structures that store and carry materials to, from, and within the Golgi Complex.

Plants have many of the same structures that animal cells do. But they also have a few things that animal cells don't.
CELL MEMBRANE
VACUOLES: Large membrane-covered chambers that store water and other liquids. Some plants wilt when their vacuoles lose water.
CHLOROPLASTS: Flattened sacs that have a double membrane and contain an important chemical called chlorophyll. Chlorophyll traps the energy of the Sun and uses it to make food. Chlorophyll is the green pigment that gives the plant its green colour.
MITOCHONDRIA
GOLGI COMPLEX

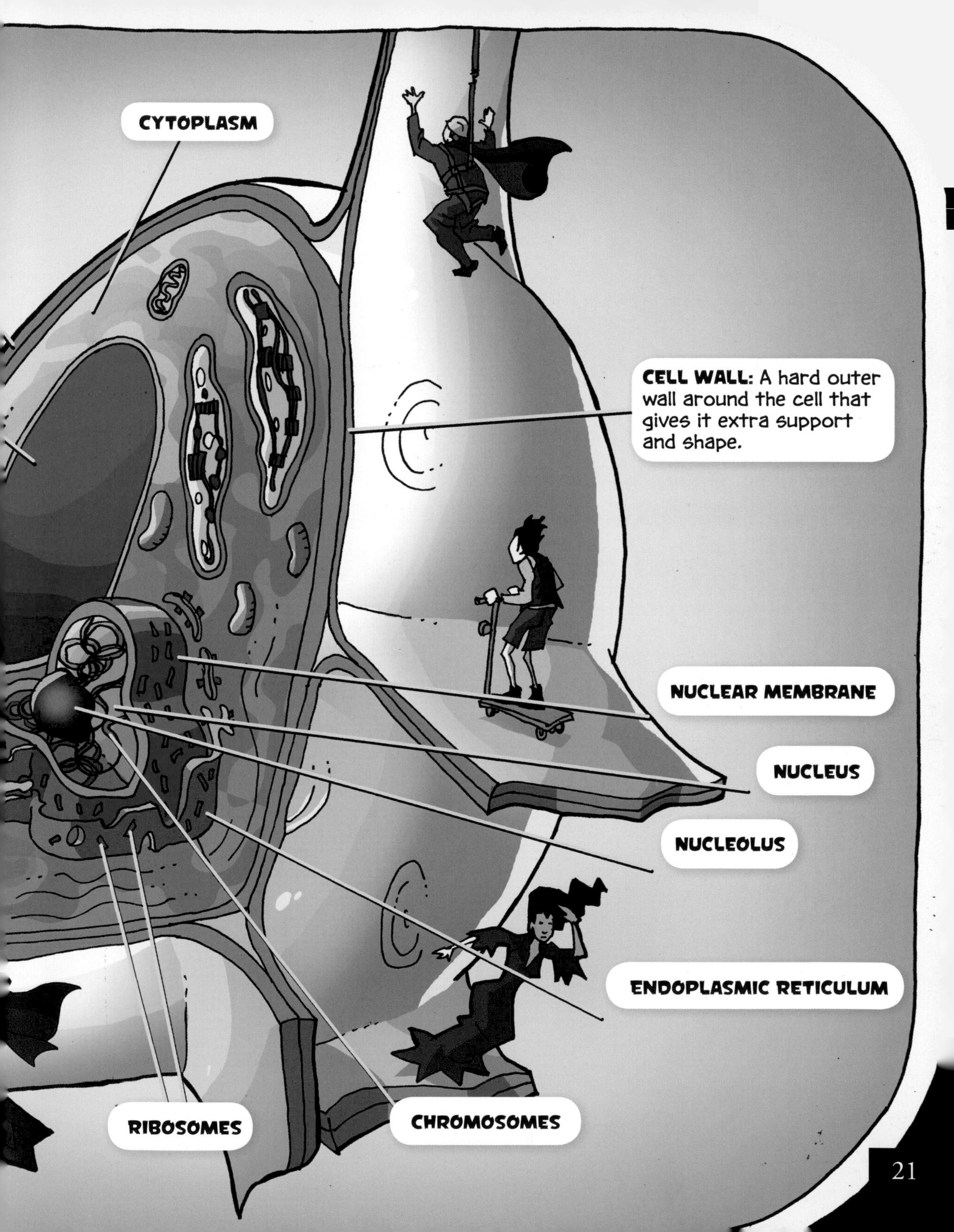
CYTOPLASM
CELL WALL: A hard outer wall around the cell that gives it extra support and shape.
NUCLEAR MEMBRANE
NUCLEUS
NUCLEOLUS
ENDOPLASMIC RETICULUM
RIBOSOMES
CHROMOSOMES

CHAPTER 4 CELLS IN ACTION

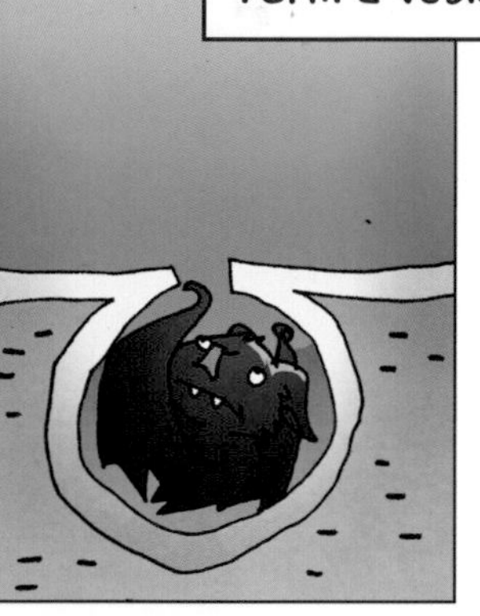

PHAGOCYTOSIS

Some cells use a special type of endocytosis called phagocytosis. The process is used when cells want to take in an entire cell, such as a bacterium. It's how white blood cells destroy germs in the blood. It's also a common way that amoebas eat.

Most living things get energy from eating food, and cells are no exception. Your body breaks down large pieces of food during digestion.
Then cells break down the food particles even more to get the stored energy. One way they do this is through cellular respiration.
DRINKING BLOOD IS EASIER!

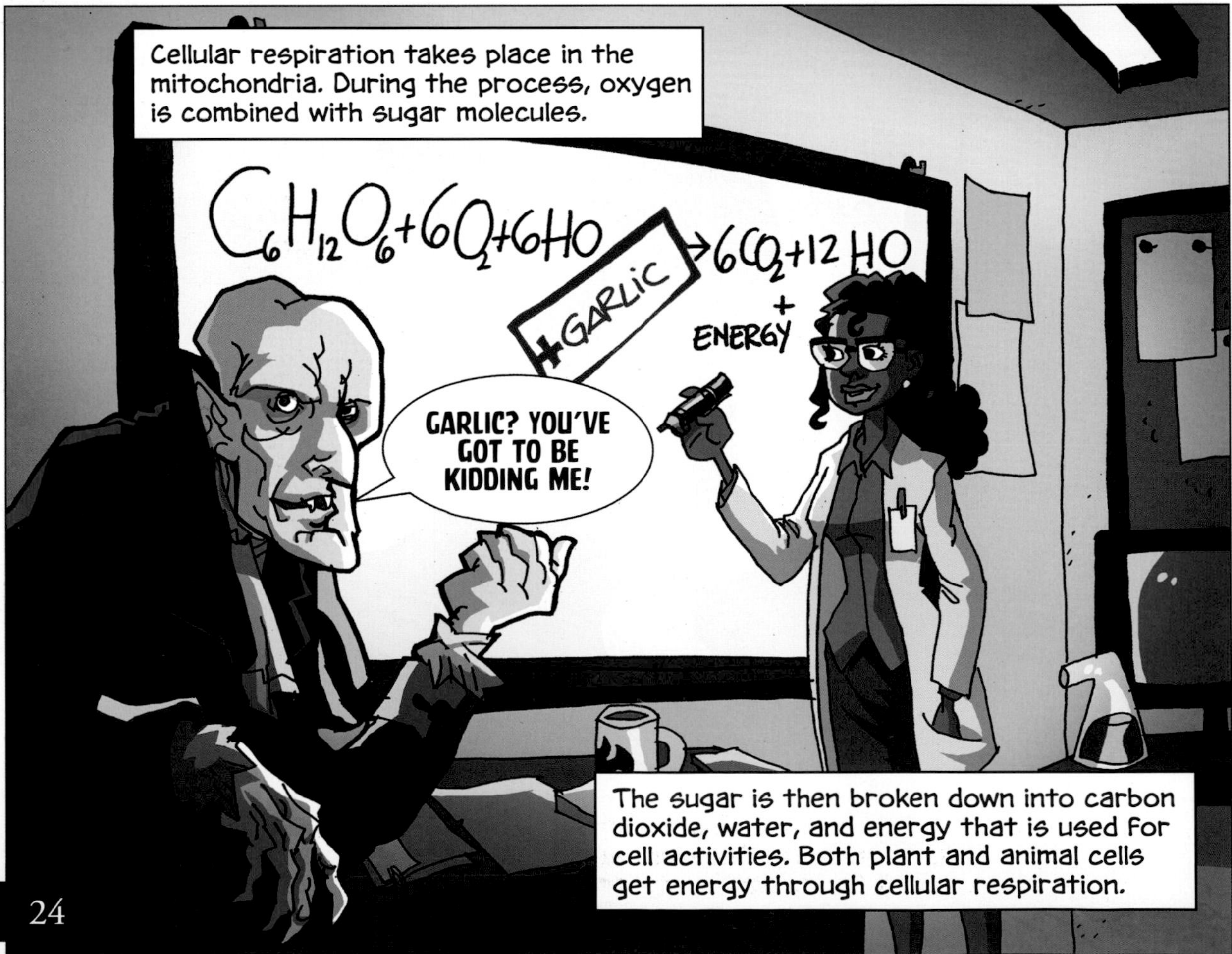
Cellular respiration takes place in the mitochondria. During the process, oxygen is combined with sugar molecules.
C6H12O6+6O2+6HO
+GARLIC
→6CO2+12 HO
+
ENERGY
GARLIC? YOU'VE GOT TO BE KIDDING ME!
The sugar is then broken down into carbon dioxide, water, and energy that is used for cell activities. Both plant and animal cells get energy through cellular respiration.

But plants also capture energy directly from the Sun. They change it into food in a process called photosynthesis.
ENERGY
During this process, plant cells use the energy captured by chlorophyll in chloroplasts. The energy is used to make sugar from carbon dioxide and water. The plant then releases oxygen as waste.
CO2
WATER

I GET MY ENERGY FROM THE SUN? NO WAY!
Plant cells use the energy in the sugar to carry on cell activity. The plant sugar also becomes a food source for animals that eat plants. The Sun is actually the main source of energy for all life forms on Earth.

binary fission form of reproduction where the DNA is copied and the cell splits into two cells

mitosis process by which the genetic material copied during interphase is separated

It's amazing to think that huge plants and animals start out as single cells. Cell division makes tiny calves grow into gigantic giraffes and little tree seedlings into huge redwoods.
WHAT A NECK!

Cell division makes babies grow into adults. And people have cells that allow them to see, think, hear, and run.

If there's life, there are cells. Every living thing is made of them. And then there are all the cells you can't see.
HEY, DON'T FORGET UNDEAD THINGS! VAMPIRES ARE MADE OF CELLS, TOO ... I THINK ...
WHOO WHOOO
We're surrounded by an incredible variety of cells of all sorts of shapes and sizes.

I LOVE YOU, RED BLOOD CELLS!
Cells are the building blocks of the most complex living things on Earth. You wouldn't be you without them!
THE END

GLOSSARY

bacteria one-celled, tiny living creatures that can be found throughout nature

binary fission form of reproduction where the DNA is copied and the cell splits into two cells

cell smallest unit of a living thing

cellular respiration process in cells by which oxygen is chemically combined with sugar molecules and energy is released

DNA genetic material that carries all of the instructions to make a living thing and keep it working; DNA stands for deoxyribonucleic acid

eukaryotic cell cell that has a membrane-bound nucleus and other organelles

mitosis during cell division, the process in which the material from the cell nucleus divides

multicellular made up of more than one cell

organelle structure in the cytoplasm of a cell that carries out specific cell activities

organism living creature

prokaryotic cell cell that does not have a membrane-bound nucleus or organelles

tissue group of different types of cells that work together to perform specific jobs

FIND OUT MORE

BOOKS

Cell Function and Specialization (Sci-Hi), Lori Johnson (Raintree, 2009)

Cells, Tissues, and Organs (The Human Machine), Richard Spilsbury (Raintree, 2008)

Investigating Cells series (Raintree, 2011)

Louis Pasteur and Pasteurization (Graphic Inventions and Discovery), Jennifer Fandel (Raintree, 2011)

Single-Celled Organisms (Sci-Hi), L. Patricia Kite (Raintree, 2009)

The Basics of Cell Life with Max Axiom, Super Scientist (Graphic Science), Amber Keyser (Raintree, 2012)

WEBSITES

www.biology4kids.com
This website has lots of useful information and clear diagrams on cell structure and functions.

www.cellsalive.com
This website has cell diagrams, animations, size comparisons, puzzles, and quizzes.

INDEX